MORE SUNSHINE
FROM BETSEY

MORE SUNSHINE FROM BETSEY

Illustrations by Betsey Clark

Edited by Aileene Herrbach Neighbors

Hallmark Crown Editions

There's so much beauty
to be found
If only we
will look around.

It seems just like magic
the way friendship brings
A holiday brightness
to everyday things.

Keeping in touch
with nice people we meet
Makes a day sunny
and ever so sweet!

Just knowing someone
cares for you
Can make the sun
come smiling through.

Laugh a little, live a little,
try a little mirth,
Sing a little, bring a little
happiness to earth!

When kind deeds
take you anywhere,
Joy is sure
to greet you there.

Pleasant times
are never gone —
They're always fun
to look back on!

Nature has
the nicest ways
Of adding beauty
to our days.

There are no finer gifts
than these —
Good friends
and happy memories.

The nicest treasure
we can find
Is to discover
peace of mind.

Memories hold close to us
All that means most to us.

Happiness is anywhere
People take the time to care!

When you wear
a cheerful smile,
You're all dressed up
in sunshine style.

Love's a present
we can give
Every single day
we live.

What a wonderful way
for a day to begin…
When a door swings wide
and a friend says,
"Come in!"

Father, we thank Thee
for the night
And for the pleasant
morning light.

Joy sings in beauty
that surrounds us…
Joy smiles through loved ones
all around us.

A good day's not measured
by hours or minutes
But by the number
of good deeds within it.

How nice to share
a cup of cheer
And a heart-to-heart
with someone dear!

Taking time
for a little fun
Is good advice
for everyone.

Nature surprises us
every day
By bringing new delights
our way!

Friendship is
a special treat
That makes our lives
especially sweet.

When we smile,
the world seems brighter.
When we smile,
our cares grow lighter.

Seeds of Kindness
that we sow
Make a Friendship Garden
grow!

Music works wonderful magic
on hearts
With the feeling of gladness
and joy it imparts.

A thoughtful deed
and friendly touch
Can tell a person,
oh, so much.

When you feel sad,
Try thinking glad.

A hug a day
Keeps the blues away.

Curiosity takes us
down a new path each day,
With lots of discoveries
along the way!

Give someone's day
a little lift —
Give a kind word
as a gift!

Trying something new
Can make a better you.

Love's the surest way
To happy-up a day.

*A word of praise
can turn a frown
Upside down.*

Dreams work like magic
to take you away
To places that you'd like
to visit someday.

No time like the present
To do something pleasant.

Happy moments are fun to spend,
Especially with a special friend.

*Life is everything
you make it.
Life is beautiful,
so take it!*

There's satisfaction
deep and true
In doing our best
at whatever we do.

*Of all the true joys
that a new day can bring,
The wonder of love
is the loveliest thing.*

Kindness to others
will always provide
A loving feeling
of warmth deep inside.

Now and then
a day of fun
Is well deserved
by everyone.

The good times
that you share with friends
Give happiness
that never ends.

Set in Gill Sans. A typeface
designed by Eric Gill in 1927.
Printed on Hallmark Eggshell Book paper.
Designed by Lavonia Harrison
and Myron McVay.